WHSmith

Challenge
Maths
KS2: Year 4
Age 8–9

**Paul Broadbent and
Peter Patilla**

Text and illustrations © Hodder Education

First published in 2007
exclusively for WHSmith by
Hodder Education
338 Euston Road
London NW1 3BH

Impression number   10 9 8 7 6 5 4 3 2 1
Year   2010 2009 2008 2007

Cover illustration by Sally Newton Illustrations

Typeset by Servis Filmsetting Ltd, Manchester

Printed and bound UK by CPI Bath

A CIP record for this book is available from the
British Library

ISBN: 978 0 340 94543 8

Parents' notes

How this book can help your child

- This book has been written for children who are between 8 and 9 years old.
- It will support and improve the work they are doing at school, whichever Maths scheme they use.
- The activities in the book have been carefully written to include the content expected of children at this stage in their development.
- The activities will help prepare your child for the different types of tests that occur in schools.

Materials needed

- Pencil, coloured pencils, eraser, watch and centimetre ruler.

Using this book

- There are 24 topics and 4 tests in the book. Each test covers 6 topics.
- Each topic is about a week's work.
- Do give help and encouragement. The activities should not be a chore.
- A calculator should not be used for the work in this book.
- Do let your child mark his or her own work under your supervision and correct any careless mistakes he or she might have made.
- When all the tests have been completed let your child fill in the Certificate of Achievement on the opposite page.
- Each double page has a title, explanation of the learning point, practice section, and challenge section.

Topic – the main learning point

Get started – helpful information and tips about the learning point

Practice – straightforward follow-up to the learning point

Challenge – uses the learning point in a slightly different way and takes it further

**This certifies
that**

_____

has completed

CHALLENGE MATHS YEAR 4

on _____

Scoring _____ on TEST 1

_____ on TEST 2

_____ on TEST 3

and _____ on TEST 4

**Total score
out of 100** _____

40–50	good effort
50–60	well done
60–70	fantastic
70–100	brilliant

Topic 1: Place value

There are ten digits:
0, **1**, **2**, **3**, **4**, **5**, **6**, **7**, **8** and **9**.

The position of a digit in a number gives its value.

The number **7283** is a four-digit number:

$$7000 + 200 + 80 + 3$$

thousands   hundreds   tens   units

Practice

1 **Write these in figures.**

a two thousand, one hundred

_____

b nine thousand, one hundred and eighty-four _____

c one thousand, four hundred and eighty _____

d six thousand, two hundred and six _____

e five thousand, six hundred and eighty _____

f four thousand, nine hundred and thirty-five _____

g eight thousand and fifty-seven

_____

h six thousand and ninety-two

_____

i three thousand and one

_____

j one thousand and nine

_____

2 **Write the missing numbers.**

a $4687 = 4000 + \underline{\quad} + 80 + 7$

b $8145 = 8000 + \underline{\quad} + \underline{\quad} + \underline{\quad}$

c $3298 = \underline{\quad} + \underline{\quad} + \underline{\quad} + \underline{\quad}$

d $6135 = \underline{\quad} + 100 + 30 + 5$

e $9387 = \underline{\quad} + \underline{\quad} + 80 + \underline{\quad}$

f $9834 = \underline{\quad} + \underline{\quad} + \underline{\quad} + \underline{\quad}$

g $1499 = 1000 + \underline{\quad} + \underline{\quad} + 9$

h $2598 = 2000 + \underline{\quad} + \underline{\quad} + \underline{\quad}$

i $4689 = \underline{\quad} + \underline{\quad} + \underline{\quad} + \underline{\quad}$

j $7894 = \underline{\quad} + 800 + \underline{\quad} + \underline{\quad}$

k $5894 = \underline{\quad} + \underline{\quad} + \underline{\quad} + 4$

l $2946 = \underline{\quad} + \underline{\quad} + \underline{\quad} + \underline{\quad}$

3 Write these numbers in order, starting with the smallest.

a 3248 4966 4769 3099 4796 ___ ___ ___ ___ ___

b 3445 3546 3080 3550 4992 ___ ___ ___ ___ ___

c 6097 6977 6009 7102 6109 ___ ___ ___ ___ ___

d 4559 4200 4560 4020 4399 ___ ___ ___ ___ ___

e 8329 8932 8900 8392 8090 ___ ___ ___ ___ ___

f 5002 5202 5222 5020 5022 ___ ___ ___ ___ ___

4 Write the value of each bold digit.

a 53 2**48** ⬭

b 3**2** 900 ⬭

c 4**6** 780 ⬭

d 17 **6**96 ⬭

e **8**7 199 ⬭

f **5**0 098 ⬭

g **4**8 144 ⬭

h 23 4**57** ⬭

i 36 790 ⬭

j 67 0**93** ⬭

k **1**0 945 ⬭

l 47 9**23** ⬭

5 Arrange these four digits to make ten different numbers.

9, 3, 8, 4

___ ___ ___ ___ ___

___ ___ ___ ___ ___

Write the numbers in order, starting with the smallest.

Topic 2: Addition facts

Get started

If you learn your addition facts, it can help with adding bigger numbers.	A quick way to add 9 is to add 10 and then take away 1:
$$5 + 8 = 13$$ $$15 + 8 = 23$$ $$50 + 80 = 130$$	$$14 + 9 \rightarrow 14 + 10 - 1 = 23$$ Use this method to add 19 or 29: $$+19 = +20 - 1$$ $$+29 = +30 - 1$$

Practice

1 Time how long it takes you to answer each block of sums.

a 3 + 8 = _____   b 5 + 9 = _____   c 14 + 5 = _____   d 6 + 14 = _____

4 + 6 = _____   8 + 6 = _____   12 + 7 = _____   7 + 12 = _____

5 + 9 = _____   3 + 7 = _____   16 + 9 = _____   9 + 19 = _____

7 + 4 = _____   5 + 8 = _____   11 + 5 = _____   7 + 14 = _____

8 + 8 = _____   6 + 6 = _____   13 + 8 = _____   5 + 18 = _____

3 + 9 = _____   8 + 9 = _____   18 + 7 = _____   3 + 19 = _____

6 + 5 = _____   4 + 6 = _____   14 + 8 = _____   7 + 16 = _____

9 + 9 = _____   8 + 3 = _____   12 + 6 = _____   4 + 19 = _____

2 Write the missing numbers. Each pair must total 100.

a 40 + ( )   b 60 + ( )   c 30 + ( )   d 70 + ( )   e 20 + ( )

f ( ) + 50   g ( ) + 80   h ( ) + 10   i ( ) + 90

3 Write the answers.

a	b	c	d
70 + 40 = ☐	90 + 40 = ☐	200 + 600 = ☐	500 + 300 = ☐
30 + 90 = ☐	60 + 50 = ☐	500 + 800 = ☐	300 + 800 = ☐
60 + 70 = ☐	80 + 70 = ☐	800 + 300 = ☐	400 + 700 = ☐
40 + 80 = ☐	90 + 50 = ☐	600 + 900 = ☐	700 + 600 = ☐

Challenge

4 **Complete these addition patterns.**

a	b	c	d	e
5 + 9 = ___	8 + 9 = ___	7 + 9 = ___	6 + 9 = ___	4 + 9 = ___
5 + 19 = ___	8 + 19 = ___	7 + 19 = ___	6 + 19 = ___	4 + 19 = ___
5 + 29 = ___	8 + 29 = ___	7 + 29 = ___	6 + 29 = ___	4 + 29 = ___
5 + 39 = ___	8 + 39 = ___	7 + 39 = ___	6 + 39 = ___	4 + 39 = ___
5 + 49 = ___	8 + 49 = ___	7 + 49 = ___	6 + 49 = ___	4 + 49 = ___

5 **Write the answers.**

a Total 8 and 7

b 900 plus 200

c Add 40 to 50

d Add 16 to 9

e Total 6, 8 and 7

f Increase 600 by 300

g 40 plus 60

h Add 19 to 8

i 9 more than 52

j Increase 38 by 3

k Increase 130 by 40

l Total 12, 9 and 6

m 5 more than 21

n 9 more than 25

6 **Look at the number machines.**
Complete each table.

a

IN		7		16		15		23	
OUT	13		18		22		27		

b

IN		8		7		11		14	
OUT	23		20		32		26		

Topic 3: Subtraction facts

Get started

If you learn your subtraction facts, it can help with taking away bigger numbers.	A quick way to take away 9 is to take away 10 and then add 1:

$$8 - 3 = 5$$
$$18 - 3 = 15$$
$$80 - 30 = 50$$

$$26 - 9 \rightarrow 26 - 10 + 1 = 17$$

Use this method to subtract 19 or 29:

$$-19 = -20 + 1$$
$$-29 = -30 + 1$$

Practice

1 Time how long it takes you to answer each block of sums.

a 17 − 6 = _____
15 − 8 = _____
16 − 9 = _____
13 − 5 = _____
18 − 7 = _____
19 − 4 = _____
14 − 6 = _____
15 − 9 = _____
18 − 5 = _____
17 − 9 = _____

b 19 − 9 = _____
13 − 7 = _____
17 − 8 = _____
14 − 5 = _____
18 − 9 = _____
16 − 7 = _____
13 − 8 = _____
19 − 5 = _____
16 − 8 = _____
15 − 7 = _____

c 24 − 8 = _____
27 − 4 = _____
26 − 9 = _____
22 − 5 = _____
23 − 6 = _____
28 − 7 = _____
24 − 6 = _____
29 − 8 = _____
21 − 5 = _____
27 − 9 = _____

d 32 − 4 = _____
35 − 7 = _____
37 − 9 = _____
33 − 8 = _____
38 − 6 = _____
36 − 8 = _____
33 − 9 = _____
34 − 5 = _____
36 − 7 = _____
35 − 6 = _____

2 Write the difference between each pair of numbers.

a 90, 40 ➤ ☐
30, 60 ➤ ☐
40, 70 ➤ ☐
90, 80 ➤ ☐
60, 20 ➤ ☐

b 190, 60 ➤ ☐
80, 150 ➤ ☐
90, 130 ➤ ☐
140, 60 ➤ ☐
50, 170 ➤ ☐

c 300, 600 ➤ ☐
500, 900 ➤ ☐
700, 200 ➤ ☐
500, 800 ➤ ☐
600, 900 ➤ ☐

d 1800, 300 ➤ ☐
500, 1600 ➤ ☐
600, 1700 ➤ ☐
1200, 900 ➤ ☐
1500, 800 ➤ ☐

Challenge

3 **Complete each of these.**

a | −9 | IN → OUT
14 | ___
18 | ___
16 | ___
17 | ___
19 | ___
13 | ___

b | −19 | IN | OUT
25 | ___
27 | ___
28 | ___
29 | ___
32 | ___
34 | ___

c | −29 | IN | OUT
32 | ___
37 | ___
39 | ___
35 | ___
43 | ___
46 | ___

d | −39 | IN | OUT
45 | ___
48 | ___
44 | ___
46 | ___
54 | ___
51 | ___

4 **Write the answers.**

a 15 subtract 7 _____

b 80 take away 30 _____

c 13 minus 8 _____

d 50 minus 20 _____

e 14 take away 6 _____

f Reduce 90 by 20 _____

g Decrease 12 by 4 _____

h 70 subtract 30 _____

i Reduce 16 by 9 _____

j The difference between 600 and 200 _____

k The difference between 8 and 19 _____

l Decrease 900 by 400 _____

5 **Complete each number trail from 100 to zero.**

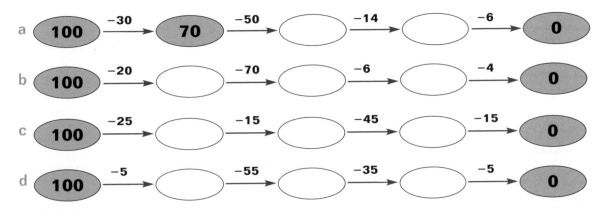

a 100 −30→ 70 −50→ ◯ −14→ ◯ −6→ 0

b 100 −20→ ◯ −70→ ◯ −6→ ◯ −4→ 0

c 100 −25→ ◯ −15→ ◯ −45→ ◯ −15→ 0

d 100 −5→ ◯ −55→ ◯ −35→ ◯ −5→ 0

Topic 4: Length

Get started

Length is measured in **millimetres, centimetres, metres** and **kilometres**.

cm 1 2 3 4 5 6 7 8 9

1 kilometre (km) = 1000 metres (m)
1 metre (m) = 100 centimetres (cm)
1 centimetre (cm) = 10 millimetres (mm)

855 cm = 8.55 m

The point separates the metres from the centimetres.

Practice

1 Write these lengths.

a 5000 m = _____ km   b 10000 m = _____ km   c 3500 m = _____ km

d 500 m = _____ km   e 6 km = _____ m   f 2000 cm = _____ m

g 7.5 km = _____ m   h 525 cm = _____ m   i 200 cm = _____ m

j 7 cm = _____ mm   k 650 cm = _____ m   l 6.35 m = _____ cm

m 40 mm = _____ cm   n 1.2 km = _____ m   o 15 mm = _____ cm

2 Use a ruler to measure.

a Measure these lines in centimetres.

[ ] cm

[ ] cm

[ ] cm

[ ] cm

b Measure these in centimetres and then write each length in millimetres.

[ ] cm = [ ] mm

[ ] cm = [ ] mm

[ ] cm = [ ] mm

[ ] cm = [ ] mm

Challenge

3 Measure these pencils and write their lengths in millimetres.

a [ ] mm

b [ ] mm

c [ ] mm

d [ ] mm

4 Write the answers.

a A piece of ribbon is 45 cm long. 100 mm is cut off.
How long is the piece of ribbon now?_____

b A bus travels 4.5 km from Arnely to Boseworth.
How far does it travel in total on a return
journey?_____

c What is 500 m less than 6 km?_____

d Two shelves are 70 cm and 90 cm in length.
What is their total length in metres and
centimetres?_____

e A tree is 3.5 m tall. It doubles in height in a year.
What is its height in centimetres after a year?_____

f A family sets off to drive 480 km.
After 250 km how much further have they to go?_____

5 Look at this ruler. What is the distance between the arrows?

a   b   c   d   e   f

a a ➡ c	b b ➡ f	c d ➡ e	d a ➡ f	e c ➡ e	f b ➡ d

Topic 5: Multiplication and division facts

Get started

If you know your multiplication facts, it helps you learn the division facts.

For every fact, you can work out another three facts very easily. Look at this for the trio 4, 6 and 24:

4 × 6 = 24

6 × 4 = 24 ← Remember **6 × 4** and **4 × 6** give the same answer – it doesn't matter which way round you multiply.

24 ÷ 4 = 6

24 ÷ 6 = 4

Practice

1 Write the missing numbers for each trio.

a ⟨**7, 5, 35**⟩ ⟨__ × 7 = __⟩ ⟨__ × __ = 35⟩ ⟨35 ÷ __ = __⟩ ⟨__ ÷ 7 = __⟩

b ⟨**4, 9, 36**⟩ ⟨__ × 4 = __⟩ ⟨__ × __ = 36⟩ ⟨36 ÷ __ = __⟩ ⟨__ ÷ 4 = __⟩

c ⟨**3, 6, 18**⟩ ⟨__ × 3 = __⟩ ⟨__ × __ = 18⟩ ⟨18 ÷ __ = __⟩ ⟨__ ÷ 3 = __⟩

d ⟨**6, 5, 30**⟩ ⟨__ × 6 = __⟩ ⟨__ × __ = 30⟩ ⟨30 ÷ __ = __⟩ ⟨__ ÷ 6 = __⟩

e ⟨**9, 3, 27**⟩ ⟨__ × __ = __⟩ ⟨__ × __ = __⟩ ⟨__ ÷ __ = __⟩ ⟨__ ÷ __ = __⟩

f ⟨**7, 6, 42**⟩ ⟨__ × __ = __⟩ ⟨__ × __ = __⟩ ⟨__ ÷ __ = __⟩ ⟨__ ÷ __ = __⟩

g ⟨**8, 9, 72**⟩ ⟨__ × __ = __⟩ ⟨__ × __ = __⟩ ⟨__ ÷ __ = __⟩ ⟨__ ÷ __ = __⟩

2 Time how long it takes you to answer each block.
Try to beat your best time.

a	b	c	d
9 × 5 = ____	3 × 6 = ____	35 ÷ 5 = ____	36 ÷ 6 = ____
6 × 4 = ____	6 × 7 = ____	21 ÷ 7 = ____	32 ÷ 8 = ____
8 × 8 = ____	5 × 4 = ____	45 ÷ 9 = ____	28 ÷ 4 = ____
3 × 9 = ____	4 × 8 = ____	30 ÷ 6 = ____	36 ÷ 9 = ____
3 × 8 = ____	7 × 7 = ____	24 ÷ 8 = ____	21 ÷ 3 = ____
4 × 6 = ____	3 × 7 = ____	18 ÷ 3 = ____	14 ÷ 7 = ____
6 × 5 = ____	5 × 8 = ____	45 ÷ 5 = ____	20 ÷ 5 = ____

3 Complete each table for these machines.

a

IN	4		7		5	
OUT		18		54		48

b

IN		6		7		4
OUT	45		18		81	

c

IN	28		36		16	
OUT		3		8		5

d

IN		21		15		24
OUT	6		9		4	

4 Complete these grids.

a

×	6	8	4
3	18		
9			
2			

b

×	4	9	3
8			
7			
5			

c

×	4	6	7
2			
5			
8			

d

×	4		8
	8	10	
3	12		24
6		30	

e

×	3	7	
4		28	36
	21		63
	24	56	

f

×		6	
	12	18	30
5	20		50
	40	60	100

Get started

A **polygon** is any 2D shape with straight sides. The sides and angles of a **regular polygon** are all equal. These are the names of some polygons.

Triangle	3 sides		**Heptagon**	7 sides	
Quadrilateral	4 sides		**Octagon**	8 sides	
Pentagon	5 sides		**Nonagon**	9 sides	
Hexagon	6 sides		**Decagon**	10 sides	

Some shapes have more than one name.

For example a **rectangle** is a quadrilateral with four right angles.

A **square** is a special rectangle because the four sides are equal.

Practice

1. Write one name for each shape. Tick the regular polygons.

a \
b \
c \
d \
e

f \
g \
h \
i \
j

k \
l \
m \
n \
o

Challenge

2 Tick the odd one out in each set. Complete each sentence.

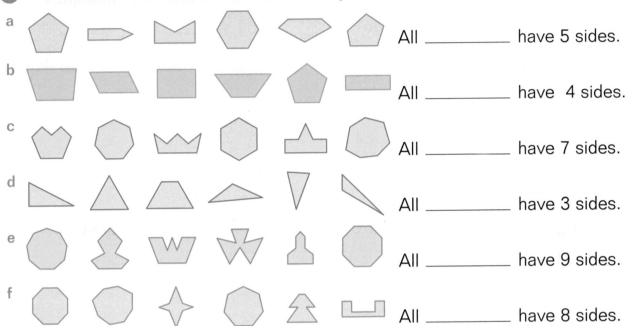

a   All _____ have 5 sides.

b   All _____ have 4 sides.

c   All _____ have 7 sides.

d   All _____ have 3 sides.

e   All _____ have 9 sides.

f   All _____ have 8 sides.

3 Join each shape to its correct place on the Carroll diagram.

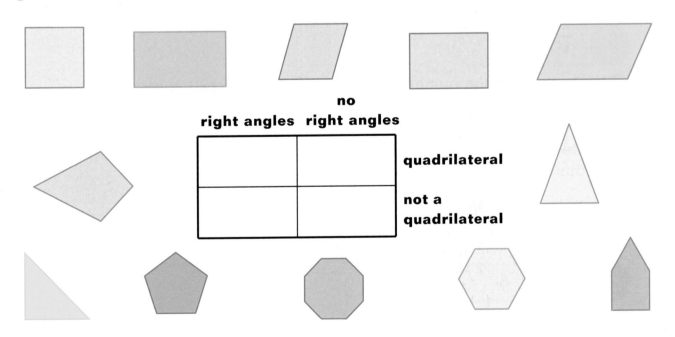

right angles | no right angles

quadrilateral

not a quadrilateral

Test 1 (Score 1 mark for every correct answer.)

Topic 1

1 Write this in figures:

six thousand and forty-seven ☐

2 Write the missing numbers.

$7264 = $ _____ $ + $ _____ $ + 60 + 4$

3 Write these in order starting with the smallest.

6704 7064 6740 7604 6047

_____ _____ _____ _____ _____

4 Write the value of the bold digit:

62 078 _____

Topic 2

5 Complete this addition pattern:

$5 + 9 = $ ☐

$15 + 9 = $ ☐

$25 + 9 = $ ☐

6 Write the missing number.

☐ $ + 7 = 15$

7 Write the total. $40 + 80 = $ ☐

8 What is the total of 5, 8 and 7? ☐

Topic 3

9 Write the missing number.

☐ $ - 7 = 6$

10 What is 120 subtract 50?

☐

11 Write the number coming out of this machine.

IN 35 → [−19] → ☐

12 Write the difference between this pair of numbers.

1500, 600 → ☐

Topic 4

13 Write the missing lengths.

$80\,mm = $ _____ cm

$6500\,m = $ _____ km

14 Write this length in cm and mm.

_____ ☐ cm = ☐ mm

15 Write the length of this pencil. _____

16 What is the difference in length between two lines measuring 17 cm and 9 cm? ☐

Topic 5

17 Write the missing numbers for this trio:

⟨ **8, 4, 32** ⟩ ⟨ __ × 4 = __ ⟩ ⟨ __ × __ = 32 ⟩ ⟨ __ ÷ 4 = __ ⟩ ⟨ 32 ÷ __ = __ ⟩

18 Answer these. $7 \times 6 =$ ☐ $32 \div 4 =$ ☐

19 Complete the table for this machine.

IN	4	7			8	
OUT			48	72		16

20 Complete this grid.

x	3	8	
4			
		48	
9			63

Topic 6

21 Name these shapes. _____

Tick the regular shape.

22 Write two names for this shape.

_____

_____

23 Tick the odd one out.

24 Tick the right angles.

Mark the test. Remember to fill in your score on page 3.

Write your score out of 24.   ☐

Add a bonus point if you scored 20 or more.

TOTAL SCORE FOR TEST 1   ☐

Get started

Mornings and afternoons are shown by **a.m.** and **p.m.**

60 seconds = 1 minute

60 minutes = 1 hour

24 hours = 1 day

Twenty-past seven in the morning ➔ **7.20 a.m.**

Twenty-past seven in the evening ➔ **7.20 p.m.**

Practice

1 Write the time shown by each clock.

a

b

c

d

e

f

g

h

2 Draw hands to show these times.

a

b

c

d

Challenge

3 A coach takes 25 minutes between each stop. Complete the timetable.

Church Street	8.50 a.m.	9.35 a.m.	11.00 a.m.	1.05 p.m.
Marsh Lane	9.15 a.m.			
Hospital			11.50 a.m.	
Swimming pool				2.20 p.m.

4 Answer these time problems.

a A film started at the cinema at 6.35 p.m. If it lasted for 90 minutes, what time did it finish? _____

b Tom wakes up at 7.30 a.m. If school begins at 8.55 a.m., how long has he got before it starts? _____

c A football match lasts for 45 minutes each half, with a 15-minute break at half time. If the match starts at 11.30 a.m., what time will it finish?

_____

d A swimming session lasted 1 hour and 20 minutes. If it finished at 2.45 p.m., when did the session start? _____

e A car journey started at 9.45 a.m. and finished at 3.50 p.m. How long did the journey last? _____

5 These clocks are all running slow. If the real time is 4.45, how many minutes slow is each clock?

a

b

c

d

_____ minutes slow   _____ minutes slow   _____ minutes slow   _____ minutes slow

e

f

_____ minutes slow   _____ minutes slow

Topic 8: Fractions of shapes

Get started

A fraction has two parts:

$\frac{2}{3}$ ← **numerator** (top number)
← **denominator** (bottom number)

1 part out of 3 shaded.
This shows $\frac{1}{3}$.

2 parts out of 3 shaded.
This shows $\frac{2}{3}$.

Fractions that have the same value are called **equivalent fractions**.

$\frac{1}{2}$ is the same as $\frac{2}{4}$

Practice

1 Write the fraction coloured on each shape.

a ⬜ b ⬤ c ⬤ d ⬠ e ⬤ f ⬤

_____ _____ _____

g ⬠ h ⬜ i ⬤ j ⬠ k ⬤ l ⬠

_____ _____ _____

2 Write the equivalent fractions.

a $\frac{1}{\square} = \frac{\square}{6}$ b $\frac{1}{\square} = \frac{\square}{12}$ c $\frac{1}{\square} = \frac{\square}{15}$

 $\frac{1}{\square} = \frac{\square}{16}$ $\frac{1}{\square} = \frac{\square}{10}$ $\frac{1}{\square} = \frac{\square}{12}$

Challenge

3 Write the fraction shaded.

a

b

c

d

_____   _____   _____   _____

e

f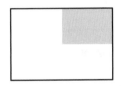

_____   _____

4 Shade these strips to show the fractions.

a $\frac{3}{4}$ b $\frac{2}{3}$ c $\frac{1}{2}$

d $\frac{2}{5}$ e $\frac{1}{3}$ f $\frac{1}{4}$

5 Write these fractions in order, starting with the smallest.

_____   _____   _____

Topic 9: Addition

Get started

There are lots of different ways to add up numbers in your head. One way is to break up numbers to make them easier to add.

For example: **46 + 37**

Try using these three steps: **1.** Hold the bigger number in your head: ◦◦◦ *46*

2. Add the tens: ◦◦◦ *46 + 30 = 76*

3. Add the units: ◦◦◦ *76 + 7 = 83*

Practice

1 **Look at these letter codes. Work out the different totals.**

| a **60** | b **40** | c **80** | d **50** | e **35** | f **55** | g **25** | h **75** |

a a + d➙ _____   b a + g➙ _____   c e + g➙ _____

d b + c➙ _____   e e + c➙ _____   f f + e➙ _____

g c + d➙ _____   h h + d➙ _____   i h + g➙ _____

j b + a➙ _____   k g + c➙ _____   l f + h➙ _____

2 **Work these out in your head.**

a 45+50 = ☐   b 60+55 = ☐   c 80+43 = ☐   d 28+70 = ☐

e 90+67 = ☐   f 42+34 = ☐   g 23+65 = ☐   h 43+36 = ☐

i 57+33 = ☐   j 61+28 = ☐   k 58+34 = ☐   l 57+25 = ☐

m 63+28 = ☐   n 42+49 = ☐   o 54+27 = ☐   p 74+52 = ☐

q 62+85 = ☐   r 55+76 = ☐   s 83+58 = ☐   t 74+68 = ☐

3 Add the rows and fill in the yellow boxes. Add the columns and fill in the pink boxes. Add the numbers in the yellow boxes, then add the numbers in the pink boxes. The two totals are the same. Write this in the blue box.

a

53	47	
28	31	

b

31	67	
42	39	

c

62	57	
38	29	

d

62	53	
74	47	

4 Join each number on the left with a number on the right to make a total of 111.

5 Write the missing digits 3 to 8 to complete these. Use each digit only once.

a $28 + \bigcirc 7 = 9\bigcirc$

b $59 + \bigcirc 4 = 1\bigcirc 3$

c $\bigcirc 1 + 6\bigcirc = 145$

23

Topic 10: Subtraction

There are lots of different ways to subtract numbers in your head.

One way is to find the difference by counting on from the smaller number.

This number line shows the method to work out **84 − 47**.

3

34

47 50   84

Count on from 47 to 50. Hold the 3 in your head.

50 to 84 is 34.

34 + 3 is 37.

So **84 − 47 = 37**

Practice

1 **Draw the jumps on the number lines to help answer these.**

a 74 − 36 = ☐

36   74

b 83 − 46 = ☐

46   83

c 61 − 37 = ☐

37   61

d 73 − 49 = ☐

49   73

e 45 − 28 = ☐

28   45

f 85 − 57 = ☐

57   85

g 72 − 46 = ☐

46   72

h 67 − 38 = ☐

38   67

i 81 − 64 = ☐

64   81

j 92 − 57 = ☐

57   92

Challenge

2 **Do these in your head.**

a 58−37 = ☐   b 74−41 = ☐   c 85−63 = ☐   d 76−32 = ☐

e 87−53 = ☐   f 52−18 = ☐   g 43−16 = ☐   h 61−14 = ☐

i 57−19 = ☐   j 72−17 = ☐   k 64−28 = ☐   l 42−25 = ☐

m 53−28 = ☐   n 56−29 = ☐   o 65−27 = ☐   p 94−57 = ☐

q 72−45 = ☐   r 85−46 = ☐   s 93−68 = ☐   t 84−58 = ☐

3 **Write the difference between the two numbers in the middle circle.**

a 36 ←◯→ 54   b 29 ←◯→ 45   c 62 ←◯→ 71   d 51 ←◯→ 67

e 28 ←◯→ 56   f 67 ←◯→ 84   g 45 ←◯→ 61   h 67 ←◯→ 92

4 **Join each number on the left with a number on the right to make a difference of 44.**

93 62 83 52 33 53   49 77 97 18 39 96

5 **Write the missing digits 3 to 8 to complete these. Use each digit only once.**

3 4 5 6 7 8

a 8◯−◯7 = 26   b 9◯−◯8 = 26   c ◯4−4◯ = 26

25

Topic 11: Sequences and patterns

Get started

A number **sequence** is a list of numbers in a pattern. To find the rule or pattern in a sequence it can help to find the differences between each pair of numbers.

$$1 \xrightarrow{+4} 5 \xrightarrow{+4} 9 \xrightarrow{+4} 13$$

The rule or pattern is **+4**

$$32 \xrightarrow{-3} 29 \xrightarrow{-3} 26 \xrightarrow{-3} 23$$

The rule or pattern is **−3**

Practice

1 Write the next three numbers in each sequence.

a	b	c	d	e	f	g	h	i	j
7	7	117	230	85	900	14	2	55	200
9	12	119	240	80	800	17	6	52	190
11	17	121	250	75	700	20	10	49	180
13	22	123	260	70	600	23	14	46	170

2 Write the missing three numbers in each sequence.

a	b	c	d	e	f	g	h	i	j
18			26	97	105		93		910
21	78		30	110	73		50	810
	73	510	34	115	64	85	53	
27	68	560		103	55	81	56	610
	63	610	42	105		77	59	
33		660		107	130	37		410

Challenge

3 Write the four missing numbers in each sequence.

a ☐, ☐, −3, −2, −1, 0, ☐, ☐

b ☐, ☐, −15, −10, −5, 0, ☐, ☐

c ☐, ☐, −4, −3, −2, −1, ☐, ☐

d ☐, ☐, −12, −9, −6, −3, ☐, ☐

e ☐, ☐, −10, −8, −6, −4, ☐, ☐

f ☐, ☐, −4, −1, 2, 5, ☐, ☐

g ☐, ☐, −7, −5, −3, −1, ☐, ☐

h ☐, ☐, −10, −6, −2, 2, ☐, ☐

4 Two numbers in each sequence have been swapped over.
Circle the two numbers.

a 28, 29, 35, 31, 32, 33, 34, 30

b 15, 19, 23, 31, 27, 35, 39

c 53, 51, 43, 47, 45, 49, 41

d 480, 478, 468, 474, 472, 470, 476

e 950, 910, 930, 920, 940, 900, 890

f 150, 149, 144, 147, 146, 145, 148

5 Follow the instructions for this number square. Look for any patterns.

- Colour the square that has number 3.
- Count on three and colour the square that has number 6.
- Keep counting on three and continue the pattern.
- Circle the number 2.
- Count on two and circle 4.
- Keep counting on two and continue the pattern.

1	2	3	4	5	6	7	8
9	10	11	12	13	14	15	16
17	18	19	20	21	22	23	24
25	26	27	28	29	30	31	32
33	34	35	36	37	38	39	40
41	42	43	44	45	46	47	48
49	50	51	52	53	54	55	56
57	58	59	60	61	62	63	64

Topic 12: Comparing and ordering numbers

Get started

When you need to put numbers in order it helps to write them under each other, lining up the units. For example:

2370
1307   **387** ⟶
438

387
438
1307
2370

We use **<** and **>** to compare numbers.

< means **is less than**
For example: **475 < 580**
475 is less than 580

> means **is greater than**
For example: **764 > 746**
764 is greater than 746

Practice

1 **Write these numbers in order, starting with the smallest.**

a 368, 860, 306, 380, 800, 806 _____ _____ _____ _____ _____ _____

b 405, 590, 450, 594, 486, 589 _____ _____ _____ _____ _____ _____

c 689, 966, 659, 965, 690, 906 _____ _____ _____ _____ _____ _____

d 215, 512, 522, 205, 505, 520 _____ _____ _____ _____ _____ _____

e 3125, 3502, 2599, 3005, 3152 _____ _____ _____ _____ _____

f 1706, 1670, 7611, 7509, 5799 _____ _____ _____ _____ _____

g 8345, 8543, 8095, 8307, 8079 _____ _____ _____ _____ _____

h 7324, 7244, 7323, 7332, 7342 _____ _____ _____ _____ _____

2 **Write the sign < or > for each pair of numbers.**

a 345 ☐ 428

b 614 ☐ 641

c 508 ☐ 505

d 617 ☐ 609

e 934 ☐ 919

f 2453 ☐ 2540

g 1800 ☐ 1798

h 4976 ☐ 4967

i 7806 ☐ 7860

Challenge

3 Write the half-way number on each of these number lines.

a 680 ⟶ [ ] ⟶ 690

b 4000 ⟶ [ ] ⟶ 4100

c 520 ⟶ [ ] ⟶ 540

d 5640 ⟶ [ ] ⟶ 5740

e 850 ⟶ [ ] ⟶ 870

f 1010 ⟶ [ ] ⟶ 1110

g 340 ⟶ [ ] ⟶ 440

h 6450 ⟶ [ ] ⟶ 6500

i 670 ⟶ [ ] ⟶ 770

j 8320 ⟶ [ ] ⟶ 8360

4 Write the signs $<$ or $>$ for these.

a 502 __ 567 __ 387   b 7400 __ 7066 __ 7060   c 2398 __ 2400 __ 2402

d 399 __ 309 __ 394   e 3654 __ 3746 __ 3577   f 6983 __ 6098 __ 5277

5 This table shows the area of some of the largest islands in Europe. Write them in size order, starting with the largest.

Island	Area (sq km)
Corsica	8 270
Crete	8 260
Cyprus	9 251
Great Britain	218 041
Iceland	103 000
Ireland	83 766
Sardinia	23 800
Sicily	25 400

Island

Topic 7

1 Write the time shown.

2 Draw hands to show this time.

3 A pizza is ordered at 7.25 p.m. If it finally arrived at 8.15 p.m., how long did it take for the pizza to be delivered?

4 A clock is 25 minutes slow. If it shows 8.35, what is the real time?

Topic 8

5 Write the fraction that is shaded.

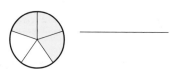 —————

6 Write the equivalent fractions.

$$\frac{1}{\square} = \frac{\square}{8}$$

7 Write the fraction that is shaded.

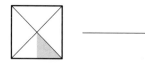 —————

8 Shade this strip to show the fraction $\frac{2}{3}$.

Topic 9

9 Write the total of these two numbers.

75 + 90 =

10 Do this in your head.

65 + 87 =

11 Add the rows, then add the columns to make the same corner total.

12 Circle the two numbers that total 125.

67   59

            58

        79

    76

Topic 10

13 Answer this.

$85 - 47 =$ ☐

14 What is the difference between 73 and 45? ☐

15 Circle the two numbers that have a difference of 48.

83   87   45   38   93

16 Write the missing digits.

$7\square - \square6 = 26$

Topic 11

17 Write the next two numbers in this sequence.

8, 13, 18, 23, ☐ , ☐

18 Write the missing numbers in this sequence.

70, 61, ☐ , 43, ☐ , 25

19 Write the four missing numbers.

☐ , ☐ , −8, −5, −2, 1, ☐ , ☐

20 Two numbers have been swapped. Circle the two numbers.

47, 45, 43, 37, 39, 41, 35

Topic 12

21 Write these numbers in order, starting with the smallest.

4769, 4799, 4679, 4767

_____ _____ _____ _____

22 Write the sign < or > for each pair of numbers.

6105 __ 6150   4355 __ 4335

23 Write the half-way number.

☐

4120 • • • • • • • • • • 4320

24 Write the sign < or > for these.

6104 ___ 3259 ___ 3260

Mark the test. Remember to fill in your score on page 3.

Write your score out of 24. ☐

Add a bonus point if you scored 20 or more.

TOTAL SCORE FOR TEST 2 ☐

Topic 13: Rounding numbers

Get started

Rounding numbers – by changing them to the nearest ten or hundred – makes them easier to work with.

It is also useful for estimating approximate answers.

Rounding to the nearest 10	**Rounding to the nearest 100**
Look at the **units** digit.	Look at the **tens** digits.
If it is 5 or more, round up the tens digit.	If it is 5 or more, round up the hundreds digit.
If it is less than 5, the tens digit stays the same.	If it is less than 5, the hundreds digit stays the same.
28<u>5</u> rounds up to 290	42<u>6</u>1 rounds up to 4300
51<u>4</u> rounds down to 510	61<u>4</u>7 rounds down to 6100

Practice

1 Round these amounts to the nearest 10.

a 456 ▸ ☐   b 283 ▸ ☐   c 149 ▸ ☐   d 305 ▸ ☐

e 644 ▸ ☐   f 838 ▸ ☐   g 1474 ▸ ☐   h 9281 ▸ ☐

2 Round these to the nearest 100.

a 673 ▸ ☐   b 457 ▸ ☐   c 145 ▸ ☐   d 565 ▸ ☐

e 816 ▸ ☐   f 937 ▸ ☐   g 4914 ▸ ☐   h 7845 ▸ ☐

3 Round these amounts to the nearest pound.

a £1.46 ▸ ☐   b £4.53 ▸ ☐   c £2.09 ▸ ☐   d £6.27 ▸ ☐

e £4.63 ▸ ☐   f £8.50 ▸ ☐   g £13.08 ▸ ☐   h £16.49 ▸ ☐

Challenge

4 Estimate which tens number each arrow points to.

a

b

c

d
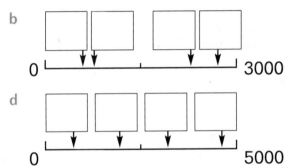

5 Estimate which hundreds number each arrow points to.

a

0 ———————— 1000

b

0 ———————— 3000

c

0 ———————— 2000

d

0 ———————— 5000

6 Estimate to give approximate answers, e.g. in a box 1 150 + 230 = 380.
The first one has been done for you.

a Round these to the nearest 10.

149 + 232 → 380

308 + 434 →

593 − 418 →

746 − 338 →

33 × 19 →

47 × 22 →

b Round these to the nearest 100.

4738 + 1229 →

6163 + 3442 →

4869 − 2345 →

7351 − 4138 →

221 × 381 →

542 × 386 →

Topic 14: Weight and mass

Weight and mass are closely linked but are not quite the same thing.

Mass is the amount of matter or material in an object.

Weight is the measurement of the force of gravity on an object.

Many books use the word 'weight' to mean the same as 'mass'.

Metric units of mass are **grams** and **kilograms**.

There are 1000 grams in 1 kilogram.

$$1000 \text{ g} = 1 \text{ kg}$$
$$500 \text{ g} = \tfrac{1}{2} \text{ kg}$$

Practice

1 Write how many grams are in each of these masses.

a $2\tfrac{1}{2}$ kg = ▢ g

b $3\tfrac{1}{4}$ kg = ▢ g

c $\tfrac{3}{4}$ kg = ▢ g

d 10.5 kg = ▢ g

e $2\tfrac{3}{4}$ kg = ▢ g

f 6.5 kg = ▢ g

2 Write these as kilograms and grams.

a 2400 g = ▢ kg ▢ g

b 1700 g = ▢ kg ▢ g

c 3550 g = ▢ kg ▢ g

d 5850 g = ▢ kg ▢ g

e 1020 g = ▢ kg ▢ g

f 4230 g = ▢ kg ▢ g

3 Write the weight of each parcel in kilograms and grams.

a   b   c   d   e   f

__ kg _____ g   __ kg _____ g   __ kg _____ g   __ kg _____ g   __ kg _____ g   __ kg _____ g

Challenge

4 Answer the problems.

a What is the total weight of parcels A and E? _____

b What is the difference in weight of parcels B and F? _____

c Which parcel is 750 g lighter than parcel C? _____

d How much heavier is parcel E than parcel B? _____

e How much lighter is parcel B than parcel C? _____

f Which two parcels have a total weight of $1\frac{1}{2}$ kg? _____

5 Round each weight to the nearest 100 g.

a 4690 g | b 5748 g | c 2685 g | d 2067 g | e 4505 g | f 3195 g

_____ g   _____ g   _____ g   _____ g   _____ g   _____ g

Topic 15: 3D shapes

Get started

3D means 3-dimensional and shows that it is a solid shape. Here are the names of some of these shapes.

cube   hemisphere   cylinder   triangular prism   tetrahedron   square-based pyramid   cuboid

We can talk about how many faces, corners (vertices) and edges a 3D shape has.

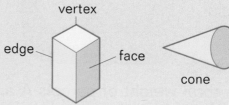

vertex   edge   face   cone   sphere

Practice

① Name each shape.

a _____

b

c _____

d _____

e _____

f _____

g _____

② Tick the odd shape out in each set.

a

b

c

d

e

Challenge

3 **How many faces are there in each of these 3D shapes?**

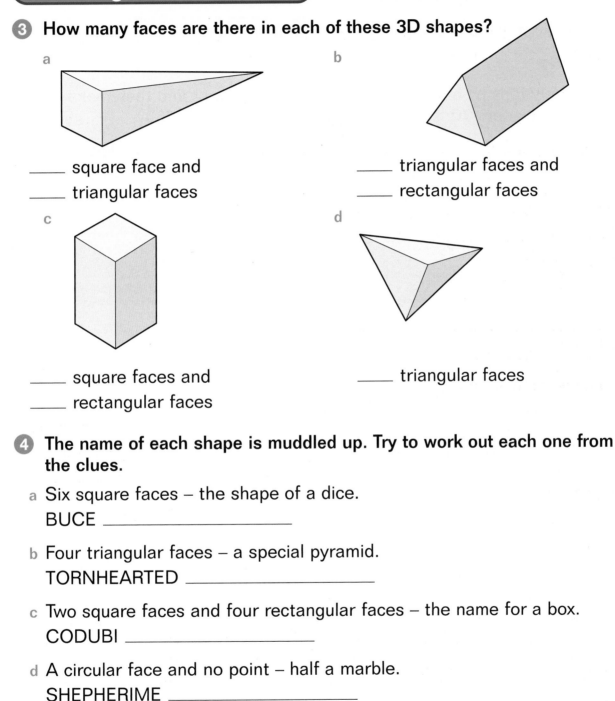

a

_____ square face and
_____ triangular faces

b

_____ triangular faces and
_____ rectangular faces

c

_____ square faces and
_____ rectangular faces

d

_____ triangular faces

4 **The name of each shape is muddled up. Try to work out each one from the clues.**

a Six square faces – the shape of a dice.
   BUCE _____

b Four triangular faces – a special pyramid.
   TORNHEARTED _____

c Two square faces and four rectangular faces – the name for a box.
   CODUBI _____

d A circular face and no point – half a marble.
   SHEPHERIME _____

Topic 16: Multiplication

Get started

Use your tables to multiply bigger numbers in your head.

Example

To multiply tens by a single digit, write the table fact and then make it ten times bigger: $70 \times 5 = 7 \times 5 \times 10 = 35 \times 10 = 350$

To multiply a 2-digit number by a single digit, break up the 2-digit number.

$$38 \times 4$$

1. Multiply the tens: $30 \times 4 = 120$

2. Multiply the units: $8 \times 4 = 32$

3. Add the two parts: $120 + 32 = 152$

Practice

1 Write the answers.

a $20 \times 3 = \boxed{}$ b $60 \times 2 = \boxed{}$ c $40 \times 5 = \boxed{}$ d $70 \times 3 = \boxed{}$ e $30 \times 4 = \boxed{}$

f $50 \times 5 = \boxed{}$ g $90 \times 6 = \boxed{}$ h $30 \times 9 = \boxed{}$ i $80 \times 4 = \boxed{}$ j $70 \times 2 = \boxed{}$

k $30 \times 8 = \boxed{}$ l $20 \times 7 = \boxed{}$ m $80 \times 3 = \boxed{}$ n $40 \times 9 = \boxed{}$ o $60 \times 4 = \boxed{}$

2 Double each number.

a **14** double →   b **17** double →   c **19** double →   d **23** double →

e **31** double →   f **28** double →   g **43** double →   h **47** double →

i **160** double →   j **250** double →   k **370** double →   l **490** double →

Challenge

3 Answer these. Do them in your head.

a 45 × 4 = ☐ b 23 × 3 = ☐ c 37 × 5 = ☐ d 24 × 3 = ☐ e 42 × 5 = ☐

f 51 × 3 = ☐ g 63 × 5 = ☐ h 58 × 2 = ☐ i 64 × 4 = ☐ j 55 × 3 = ☐

k 69 × 4 = ☐ l 74 × 5 = ☐ m 86 × 2 = ☐ n 79 × 3 = ☐ o 88 × 4 = ☐

4 Answer these problems.

a What is 43 multiplied by 6? ☐

b There are 24 hours in a day. How many hours are there in a week? ☐

c Sam scored 49 points in a game. Jo scored double Sam's score. What did Jo score? ☐

d Apples are packed with 64 to each box. How many apples are there in five boxes? ☐

e A train ticket costs £38. What is the total cost for four tickets? ☐

f What number is double 99? ☐

5 Use the grids to answer these.

a 36 × 8

x	30	6
8	240	48

= 288

b 53 × 7

x	50	3
7		

= ____

c 46 × 9

x	40	6
9		

= ____

d 78 × 6

x	70	8
6		

= ____

e 68 × 7

x	60	8
7		

= ____

f 79 × 8

x	70	9
8		

= ____

6 Write the missing digits 1 to 6 to complete these. Use each digit only once.

a 2◯ × 6 = ◯38   b ◯5 × 7 = 31◯   c ◯8 × 9 = 61◯

Topic 17: Division

Get started

Division is the inverse or opposite of multiplication.

So if you know your tables, it will help you to divide numbers.

$$7 \times 3 = 21$$

$$21 \div 3 = 7$$

$$21 \div 7 = 3$$

There are several ways of writing a division:

$$30 \div 6$$

$$\frac{30}{6}$$

$$6\overline{)30}$$

All these mean 30 divided by 6.

Sometimes divisions aren't exact and leave **remainders**.

$$20 \div 3 = 6 \text{ remainder } 2 \quad \text{or } 6r2$$

Practice

1 Write the answers.

a $24 \div 3 =$ ☐   b $18 \div 2 =$ ☐   c $45 \div 5 =$ ☐   d $30 \div 3 =$ ☐   e $28 \div 4 =$ ☐

f $60 \div 5 =$ ☐   g $42 \div 6 =$ ☐   h $32 \div 2 =$ ☐   i $60 \div 4 =$ ☐   j $54 \div 3 =$ ☐

k $72 \div 3 =$ ☐   l $76 \div 4 =$ ☐   m $85 \div 5 =$ ☐   n $78 \div 6 =$ ☐   o $92 \div 4 =$ ☐

2 Halve each number.

a 34 ➤ ☐   b 42 ➤ ☐   c 38 ➤ ☐   d 46 ➤ ☐

e 32 ➤ ☐   f 48 ➤ ☐   g 56 ➤ ☐   h 64 ➤ ☐

i 82 ➤ ☐   j 76 ➤ ☐   k 94 ➤ ☐   l 78 ➤ ☐

3 Answer these. Remember to include the remainder.

a $35 \div 4 =$ ☐ r ☐   b $26 \div 3 =$ ☐ r ☐   c $47 \div 2 =$ ☐ r ☐

d $44 \div 3 =$ ☐ r ☐   e $\frac{71}{3} =$ ☐ r ☐   f $\frac{83}{2} =$ ☐ r ☐

g $\frac{59}{4} =$ ☐ r ☐   h $\frac{74}{5} =$ ☐ r ☐   i $89 \div 6 =$ ☐ r ☐

Challenge

4 Answer these problems.

a What is 75 divided by 5? ☐

b What number is half of 98? ☐

c There are 54 children on a Cub outing.
How many groups of six children can be made? ☐

d Toby spent 84p on 6 pencils. How much was each pencil? ☐

e I have 42 cakes. Each box holds 4 cakes. How many boxes will I need? ☐

f A magazine costs £3 each month. Jack has £38.
How many magazines will he be able to get? ☐

5 Match each division to a remainder. Write a division for the spare remainder.

6 Write the missing digits 1 to 6 to complete these. Use each digit only once.

a 75 ÷ ◯ = 2◯   b 9◯ ÷ 2 = ◯6   c ◯2 ÷ 2 = ◯

Topic 18: Coordinates

Get started

Coordinates show the exact position of a point on a grid.

The coordinates of A are (2, 4)

The coordinates of B are (4, 2)

Read the **horizontal** coordinate first and then the **vertical** coordinate.

Practice

1. **Look at these points and answer the questions.**

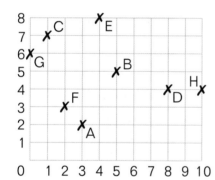

Write the coordinates of these points.

A → (___,___)   **F** → (___,___)

D → (___,___)   **H** → (___,___)

Write the letters for each of these points.

(5, 5) ☐ (0, 6) ☐ (4, 8) ☐ (1, 7) ☐

2. **Plot and label these points on the grid.**

A = (4, 1)   **B** = (6, 2)
C = (0, 1)   **D** = (5, 4)
E = (2, 0)   **F** = (8, 7)
G = (9, 3)   **H** = (7, 5)

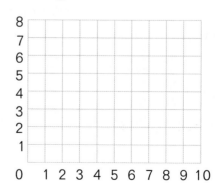

Challenge

③ Plot these points on the grid.

Use a ruler to join up the points in order to draw a shape.

A = (3, 4)   B = (4, 6)

C = (5, 4)   D = (7, 3)

E = (5, 2)   F = (4, 0)

G = (3, 2)   H = (1, 3)

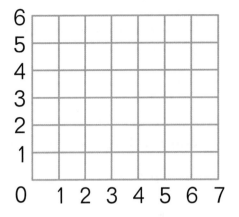

④ Design your own star on this grid.

Write the coordinates to show the position of each point.

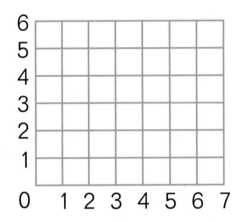

⑤ Here are three corners of a rectangle.

a What are the coordinates of the three corners?

A → (___,___) **B** → (___,___) **C** → (___,___)

b What would be the coordinates of the fourth corner, **D**? (___,___)

c Plot point **D** and complete the rectangle.

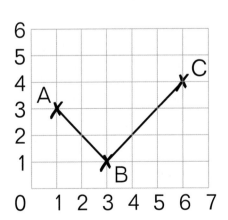

Test 3 (Score 1 mark for every correct answer.)

Topic 13

1 Round these to the nearest 10.

543 ▸ ☐

6446 ▸ ☐

2 Round these to the nearest 100.

752 ▸ ☐

3148 ▸ ☐

3 Round these to the nearest pound.

£3.62 ▸ ☐

£24.50 ▸ ☐

4 Estimate which tens number each arrow points to.

0 └─────────────┘ 200

Topic 14

5 Write the missing amount.

$8\frac{1}{10}$ kg = ☐ g

6 Write this as kilograms and grams.

6225 g = ☐ kg ☐ g

7 What is the weight of this parcel?

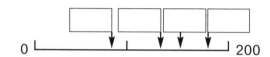

_____ kg _____ g

8 What is the total weight of these two parcels?

250 g   2¾ kg

_____ kg _____ g

Topic 15

9 Name this shape.

_____

10 Tick the odd shape out.

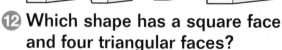

11 How many faces has this shape?

_____ hexagonal faces

_____ rectangular faces

12 Which shape has a square face and four triangular faces?

_____

Topic 16

13 Write the answer.

$70 \times 4 = \boxed{}$

14 What is double 56? $\boxed{}$

15 Answer this mentally.

$83 \times 3 = \boxed{}$

16 Bulbs are packed in boxes of six. How many bulbs are there in 25 boxes? $\boxed{}$

Topic 17

17 Write the answer.

$64 \div 4 = \boxed{}$

18 What is half of 76? $\boxed{}$

19 Answer this.

$4\overline{)78} = \boxed{}$ r $\boxed{}$

20 Callum has 81p. He buys five ice lollies and gets 1p change. How much does each ice lolly cost? $\boxed{}$

Topic 18

Look at these points and answer the questions.

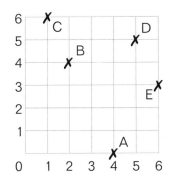

21 Write the coordinates for A (___,___)

22 Write the letter at position (1, 6) $\boxed{}$

23 Write the coordinates for E (___,___)

24 Draw a cross at position (3, 5).

Mark the test. Remember to fill in your score on page 3.

Write your score out of 24. $\boxed{}$

Add a bonus point if you scored 20 or more.

TOTAL SCORE FOR TEST 3 $\boxed{}$

Get started

A decimal point is used to separate whole numbers from fractions.

27.43

tens   units   tenths   hundredths

$\frac{1}{10} = 0.1$ $\frac{1}{2} = 0.5$

$\frac{2}{10} = 0.2$ $\frac{1}{100} = 0.01$

Practice

1 Write these as decimals.

a $\frac{3}{10}$ ▸ ☐   b $\frac{9}{10}$ ▸ ☐   c $\frac{7}{10}$ ▸ ☐   d $\frac{1}{2}$ ▸ ☐

e $\frac{4}{10}$ ▸ ☐   f $\frac{8}{10}$ ▸ ☐   g $4\frac{1}{2}$ ▸ ☐   h $2\frac{1}{10}$ ▸ ☐

i $3\frac{7}{10}$ ▸ ☐   j $5\frac{3}{10}$ ▸ ☐   k $6\frac{9}{10}$ ▸ ☐   l $4\frac{2}{10}$ ▸ ☐

2 Write the decimals on these lines.

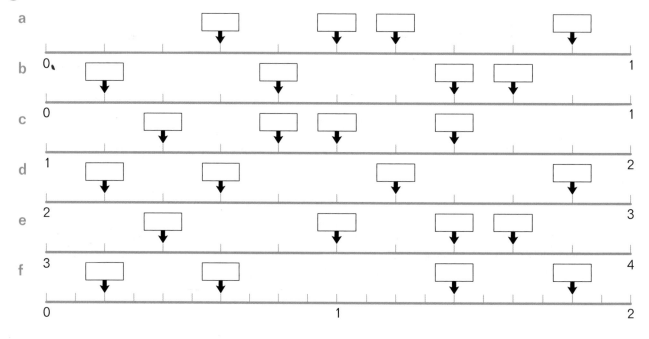

Challenge

3 Write the value of the bold digit as a fraction.

a 0.3**5** ☐   b 6.**8** ☐   c 14.7**5** ☐   d 0.0**2** ☐   e 9.**3**6 ☐

f 8.0**7** ☐   g 15.**6**9 ☐   h 4.1**5** ☐   i 10.**8** ☐   j 16.**4**7 ☐

4 Put in the signs < or > so that these are true.

a 4.65 kg ☐ 4.70 kg   b 5.80 m ☐ 5.18 m   c £3.65 ☐ £3.56

d 3.25 ☐ 3.2   e 3.15 ☐ 3.5   f 6.05 ☐ 6.5

g 2.34 ☐ 2.43   h 8.66 ☐ 8.07

5 Write these numbers in order, starting with the smallest.

a

3.8   3.6   2.9   4   3   3.1   0.9

____ ____ ____ ____ ____ ____ ____

b

4.8   8.32   0.8   8.3   0.4   4   8.1

____ ____ ____ ____ ____ ____ ____

c

2.71   7.17   2   2.1   7.6   2.93   2.6

____ ____ ____ ____ ____ ____ ____

d

10.35   10.14   10.4   3.06   11.1   10   3

____ ____ ____ ____ ____ ____ ____

Topic 20: Capacity

Get started

Capacity is about how much something holds.

Metric units of capacity are litres and millilitres.

ml is short for millilitre.

l is short for litre.

There are **1000 millilitres** in **1 litre**.

1000 ml = 1 l

500 ml = $\frac{1}{2}$ l

100 ml = $\frac{1}{10}$ l

Practice

1 Write how many millilitres are in each of these capacities.

a $1\frac{1}{2}$ l = _____ ml   b $2\frac{1}{4}$ l = _____ ml   c $\frac{1}{4}$ l = _____ ml   d $2\frac{1}{10}$ l = _____ ml

e 6.5 l = _____ ml   f $4\frac{3}{4}$ l = _____ ml   g 8.5 l = _____ ml   h $12\frac{3}{10}$ l = _____ ml

2 Write these as litres and millilitres.

a 4300 ml = _____ l _____ ml   b 1900 ml = _____ l _____ ml

c 6550 ml = _____ l _____ ml   d 2350 ml = _____ l _____ ml

e 2020 ml = _____ l _____ ml   f 6730 ml = _____ l _____ ml

g 4525 ml = _____ l _____ ml   h 1975 ml = _____ l _____ ml

3 Write the amount shown in each jug.

a _____ ml   b _____ ml   c _____ ml   d _____ ml   e _____ ml

f _____ ml   g _____ ml   h _____ ml   i _____ ml   j _____ ml

Challenge

4 Answer the problems.

a What is the total capacity of containers A and E?

b What is the difference in capacity of containers F and D?

c Which container has double the capacity of container B?

d How much more does container E hold than container F?

e How much less does container A hold than container D?

f Which two containers have a total capacity of 2 litres?

5 Round these to the nearest 100 ml.

Topic 21: Fractions of amounts

Fractions have a **numerator** and a **denominator**.

$\frac{1}{3}$ of 6 is the same as 6 ÷ 3 = 2

1 ←**numerator** (top number)
3 ←**denominator** (bottom number)

The denominator shows the number of equal parts.

The numerator shows the number of those parts you are dealing with.

Practice

1 **Work out the fraction of each amount.**

a Colour $\frac{1}{2}$ of the circles and write the answer.

○ ○ ○ ○ ○ ○ $\frac{1}{2}$ of 6 = ☐

○ ○ ○ ○ ○ ○ ○ ○ ○ ○ $\frac{1}{2}$ of 10 = ☐

○ ○ ○ ○ ○ ○ ○ ○ $\frac{1}{2}$ of 8 = ☐

○ ○ ○ ○ ○ ○ ○ ○ ○ ○ ○ ○ $\frac{1}{2}$ of 12 = ☐

b Colour $\frac{1}{4}$ of the circles and write the answer.

○ ○ ○ ○ ○ ○ ○ ○ $\frac{1}{4}$ of 8 = ☐

○ ○ ○ ○ ○ ○ ○ ○ ○ ○ ○ ○ ○ ○ ○ ○ $\frac{1}{4}$ of 16 = ☐

○ ○ ○ ○ $\frac{1}{4}$ of 4 = ☐

○ ○ ○ ○ ○ ○ ○ ○ ○ ○ ○ ○ $\frac{1}{4}$ of 12 = ☐

2 **Answer each of these.**

a

$\frac{1}{3}$ of ...
15 →
12 →
21 →
18 →
30 →

b

$\frac{1}{5}$ of ...
20 →
15 →
30 →
40 →
25 →

c

$\frac{1}{4}$ of ...
20 →
32 →
24 →
40 →
36 →

d

$\frac{1}{10}$ of ...
30 →
80 →
70 →
60 →
100 →

Challenge

3 Answer these.

 1p 2p 5p 10p 20p 50p £1

a	What fraction of £1 is:
	50p →
	20p →
	10p →
	25p →
	75p →

b	What fraction of £2 is:
	20p →
	£1 →
	50p →
	£1.50 →
	40p →

c	What fraction of £10 is:
	£2.50 →
	£5 →
	£1 →
	£7.50 →
	£2 →

4 Answer these.

a	What fraction of 1 kilogram is:
	100 g →
	400 g →
	200 g →
	500 g →
	300 g →

b	What fraction of 1 litre is:
	250 ml →
	750 ml →
	600 ml →
	800 ml →
	700 ml →

c	What fraction of 1 metre is:
	50 cm →
	25 cm →
	10 cm →
	75 cm →
	20 cm →

5 **Colour this grid to make a pattern.**
Use these fractions for each colour.

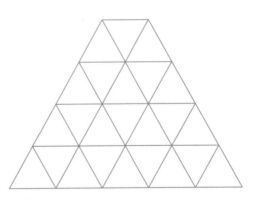

$\frac{1}{4}$ red

$\frac{1}{6}$ blue

$\frac{1}{12}$ yellow

$\frac{1}{3}$ green

$\frac{1}{8}$ orange

How many triangles are left white? _____

Topic 22: Graphs

Pictograms are graphs that have pictures.

Each picture stands for a number. Look at the **key** to see how many each picture stands for.

Some graphs have **bars** or **columns**.

The axes have **labels** that give you information.

You must look carefully at the numbered axis to see what **scale** is being used.

The scale does not always go up in ones.

Practice

1 This pictogram shows the number of visitors to a museum in a week.

Look at the pictogram and answer these questions.

Key

represents 5 visitors

represents between 1 and 5 visitors

Days: Mon, Tues, Wed, Thurs, Fri, Sat, Sun

a How many visitors went to the museum on Tuesday? _____

b On which day did 37 people visit the museum? _____

c On which two days did the same number of people visit the museum?

_____

d Approximately how many people visited the museum on Thursday? _____

e On which two days were there fewer visitors than on Monday?

_____

f 14 of the visitors on Tuesday were children. How many adults were there on Tuesday? _____

g 88 people visited the museum at the weekend. How many visited on Saturday? _____

h Why do you think there were no visitors on Wednesday?

_____

Challenge

2 **This bar chart shows the number of bikes sold each month by a bike shop.**

Use the graph to answer these questions.

a How many bikes were sold in June? _____

b In which month were the most bikes sold? _____

c In which month were 56 bikes sold? _____

d How many bikes were sold in total in July and August? _____

e In which month were half the number of bikes sold compared to December? _____

3 **This table of results shows the times of six riders in a cycle race. Complete the graph and answer the questions.**

Alan	Ben	Chris	David	Eric	Fred
48 mins	52 mins	39 mins	46 mins	43 mins	40 mins

a Who had the fastest time? _____

b Which cyclist finished six minutes behind Fred? _____

c Which cyclist finished nine minutes ahead of Ben? _____

d Write the cyclists in the order they finished.

1_____ 2 _____

3_____ 4 _____

5_____ 6 _____

Topic 23: Money

Get started

There are 100 pence in £1. When we write amounts as pounds and pence, we separate the pounds from the pence with a decimal point.

£1.40 = 140p   £3.09 = 309p
£5.38 = 538p   £0.85 = 85p

Practice

1 Write these totals.

a (20p)(5p)(10p)(5p) _____ p

b (1p)(2p)(20p)(50p) _____ p

c (10p)(20p)(1p)(2p) _____ p

d (5p)(5p)(5p)(5p) _____ p

e (10p)(1p)(20p)(50p) _____ p

f (20p)(50p)(10p)(10p) _____ p

g (1p)(5p)(50p)(1p) _____ p

h (20p)(10p)(20p)(20p) _____ p

i (2p)(2p)(50p)(20p) _____ p

j (10p)(10p)(2p)(50p) _____ p

2 Write these amounts in a different way.

a £1.25 ⇒ _____ p
b £3.49 ⇒ _____ p
c £2.08 ⇒ _____ p
d £14.99 ⇒ _____ p

e £12.81 ⇒ _____ p
f £23.06 ⇒ _____ p
g 149p ⇒ £_____
h 227p ⇒ £_____

i 503p ⇒ £_____
j 1231p ⇒ £_____
k 66 ⇒ £_____
l 69p ⇒ £_____

3 Write the change from each of these.

a

Change from	£1
48p➤	85p➤
37p➤	64p➤
91p➤	29p➤

b

Change from	£5
£4.30➤	£2.89➤
£3.21➤	£4.06➤
£2.97➤	£1.84➤

c

Change from	£10
£8.75➤	£9.22➤
£6.99➤	£4.83➤
£7.56➤	£8.47➤

Challenge

④ Answer these problems.

a Jo buys four pairs of socks at 80p a pair.
How much change does she get from £5? _____

b How many 8p sweets can David buy with 70p? _____

c What is the total cost of four stamps at 30p and six stamps at 42p? _____

d What is the change from £10 for six videos at £1.20 each? _____

e Doughnuts cost £1.09 a pack. What is the cost of three packs? _____

f CDs cost £7.49 in the sales. What change from
£20 will there be for two CDs? _____

⑤ Answer these.

Cheese & Pickle £1.24

Sausage roll 63p each

Samosa 38p each

a How much will three sausage rolls cost? _____

b What is the total cost of a cheese and pickle sandwich and
two sausage rolls? _____

c How much will ten samosas cost? _____

d What is the change from £5 for two cheese and pickle sandwiches
and a samosa? _____

⑥ A magazine costs £1.28.

1p 2p 5p 20p £1

£1.28
MAGAZINE OF
THE MONTH

The smallest number of coins needed to pay for
it exactly is 5.

a Write four other amounts that need exactly 5 of
any coins.

_____

b Write four amounts that need exactly 6 of any coins.

_____

c What is the lowest amount that you can make with 6 different coins? [   ]

Topic 24: Angles

Get started

Angles are measures of turn. They are measured in **degrees**.

- A complete turn is 360°
- Half a complete turn is 180°. This looks like a straight line
- A quarter turn is 90°, also called a right angle.
- The three angles of an equilateral triangle are 60° each.
- Half a right angle is 45°.

There are 8 compass directions:

North, North-east, East, South-east, South, South-west, West, North-west

clockwise   anticlockwise

Practice

1 These angles show either 360°, 180°, 90°, 60° or 45°.

Write the size of each angle.

a ____ b ____ c ____

d ____ e ____ f ____ g ____

h ____ i ____ j ____

2 Write where you will face after each turn: N, S, E or W.

Face North to start each time

a Turn 180° clockwise. ____
b Tum 90° anticlockwise. ____
c Turn 45° clockwise. ____

Face East to start each time

g Make 360° turn anticlockwise. ____
h Make 90° turn clockwise. ____
i Make 45° turn anticlockwise. ____

Face South to start each time

d Turn 90° anticlockwise. ____
e Turn 45° clockwise. ____
f Turn 180° clockwise. ____

Face West to start each time

j Make 180° turn clockwise. ____
k Make 45° turn clockwise. ____
l Make 90° turn anticlockwise. ____

Challenge

3 Tick the right angles on these shapes.

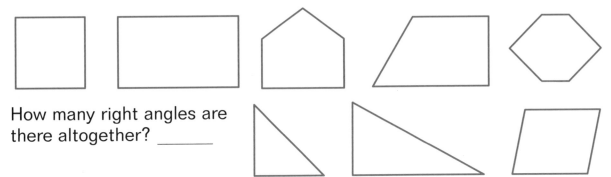

How many right angles are there altogether? _____

4 Write these angles in order of size, starting with the smallest.

A   B   C   D   E   F

_____ _____ _____ _____ _____

5 Look at this dial from a washing machine.

The arrow turns clockwise. Answer these questions.

a How many degrees does the arrow turn from:

pre-wash to spin _____

wash to rinse _____

rinse to off _____

pre-wash to dry_____

b Write the position the arrow is pointing to after these turns:

60° from pre-wash _____

120° from spin _____

180° from wash _____

360° from off _____

Test 4 (Score 1 mark for every correct answer.)

1 Write these as decimals.

$\frac{3}{10}$ = ☐ $\frac{1}{2}$ = ☐

2 Write the decimals on this line.

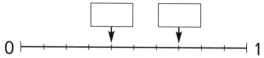

0 ├──┼──┼──┼──┼──┼──┼──┤ 1

3 What is the value of the digit 5 in this number?

12.57 ☐

4 Write the correct signs < or > for these.

4.6 ☐ 4.8 ☐ 4.3

5 Write the missing amount.

$3\frac{1}{10}$ litres = _____ ml

6 Write this as litres and millilitres.

4805 ml = ____ l _____ ml

7 How much liquid is in this jug?

____ l _____ ml

8 What is the difference between these two amounts? _____

$1\frac{1}{2}$ l   800 ml

9 Circle $\frac{1}{3}$ of the stars and write the answer.

$\frac{1}{3}$ of 12 = ☐

10 What is one-fifth of 30? ____

11 What fraction of £2 is 50p? ☐

12 What fraction of 1 kilogram is 750 g? ☐

Topic 22

This bar chart shows a survey of the pets owned by a group of people.

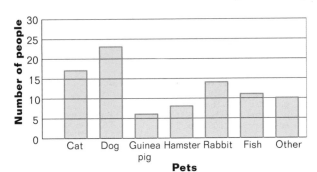

13 How many people had a dog?

_____

14 Which pet was owned by 14 people? _____

15 How many more people owned a cat than a fish? _____

16 How many guinea pigs and hamsters were there altogether?

_____

Topic 23

17 Write the total.

20p

2p

50p

5p

[ ] p

18 Write these amounts.

£3.76 = _____ p

1245p = £_____

19 A T-shirt costs £6.89. What change would be given from £10? [ ]

20 Harry bought six felt-pens for 96p. How much would two felt-pens cost? [ ]

Topic 24

21 Write the size of this angle. _____ °

0

22 Tick the right angles on this shape.

23 If you face North and turn anticlockwise by 45°, which direction will you now be facing? _____

24 Tick the angle that shows 60°.

Mark the test. Now add up all your test scores and put your final score on page 3.

Write your score out of 24. [ ]

Add a bonus point if you scored 20 or more.

TOTAL SCORE FOR TEST 4 [ ]

Answers

Topic 1: **Place value** (page 4)

1.
a. 2100 **b.** 9184
c. 1480 **d.** 6206
e. 5680 **f.** 4935
g. 8057 **h.** 6092
i. 3001 **j.** 1009

2.
a. 600
b. 100 + 40 + 5
c. 3000 + 200 + 90 + 8 **d.** 6000
e. 9000 + 300 + 7 **f.** 9000 + 800 + 30 + 4
g. 400 + 90 **h.** 500 + 90 + 8
i. 4000 + 600 + 80 + 9 **j.** 7000 + 90 + 4
k. 5000 + 800 + 90 **l.** 2000 + 900 + 40 + 6

3.
a. 3099, 3248, 4769, 4796, 4966
b. 3080, 3445, 3546, 3550, 4992
c. 6009, 6097, 6109, 6977, 7102
d. 4020, 4200, 4399, 4559, 4560
e. 8090, 8329, 8392, 8900, 8932
f. 5002, 5020, 5022, 5202, 5222

4.
a. 40 **b.** 2000 **c.** 6000
d. 600 **e.** 80 000 **f.** 50 000
g. 40 000 **h.** 50 **i.** 6000
j. 90 **k.** 10 000 **l.** 20

5. Any 10 of these numbers:
3489 3498 3849 3894 3948 3984
4389 4398 4839 4893 4938 4983
8349 8394 8439 8493 8934 8943
9348 9384 9438 9483 9834 9843

Topic 2: **Addition facts** (page 6)

1.

a.	b.	c.	d.
11	14	19	20
10	14	19	19
14	10	25	28
11	13	16	21
16	12	21	23
12	17	25	22
11	10	22	23
18	11	18	23

2.
a. 60
b. 40
c. 70
d. 30
e. 80
f. 50
g. 20
h. 90
i. 10

3.

a.	b.
110	130
120	110
130	150
120	140
c. 800	**d.** 800
1300	1100
1100	1100
1500	1300

4.

a.	b.	c.
14	17	16
24	27	26
34	37	36
44	47	46
54	57	56
d. 15	**e.** 13	
25	23	
35	33	
45	43	
55	53	

5.
a. 15 **b.** 1100
c. 90 **d.** 25
e. 21 **f.** 900
g. 100 **h.** 27
i. 61 **j.** 41
k. 170 **l.** 27
m. 26 **n.** 34

6.
a.

IN	4	7	9	16	13	15	18	23
OUT	13	16	18	25	22	24	27	32

b.

IN	4	8	1	7	13	11	7	14
OUT	23	27	20	26	32	30	26	33

Topic 3: **Subtraction facts** (page 8)

1.

a.	b.	c.	d.
11	10	16	28
7	6	23	28
7	9	17	28
8	9	17	25
11	9	17	32
15	9	21	28
8	5	18	24
6	14	21	29
13	8	16	29
8	8	18	29

2.
a. 50
30
30
10
40
b. 130
70
40
80
120
c. 300
400
500
300
300
d. 1500
1100
1100
300
700

Topic 4: **Length** (page 10)

1.
a. 5 km **b.** 10 km **c.** 3.5 km
d. 0.5 km **e.** 6000 m **f.** 20 m
g. 7500 m **h.** 5.25 m **i.** 2 m
j. 70 mm **k.** 6.5 m **l.** 635 cm
m. 4 cm **n.** 1200 m **o.** 1.5 cm

2.
a. 6 cm
4 cm
5 cm
3 cm
b. 4.5 cm, 45 mm
2.5 cm, 25 mm
6.5 cm, 65 mm
5.5 cm, 55 mm

3.
a. 55 mm
b. 47 mm
c. 64 mm
d. 37 mm

4.
a. 35 cm
b. 9 km
c. 5.5 km
d. 1 m 60 cm
e. 700 cm
f. 230 km

5.
a. 3 cm
b. 12 cm
c. 4.5 cm
d. 13.5 cm
e. 8 cm
f. 5 cm

3.

a.	b.	c.	d.
5	6	3	6
9	8	8	9
7	9	10	5
8	10	6	7
10	13	14	15
4	15	17	12

4.
a. 8 **b.** 50
c. 5 **d.** 30
e. 8 **f.** 70
g. 8 **h.** 40
i. 7 **j.** 400
k. 11 **l.** 500

5.
a. 20, 6
b. 80, 10, 4
c. 75, 60, 15
d. 95, 40, 5

Topic 5: **Multiplication and division facts** (page 12)

1.
a. $5 \times 7 = 35$ $7 \times 5 = 35$ $35 \div 5 = 7$ $35 \div 7 = 5$
b. $9 \times 4 = 36$ $4 \times 9 = 36$ $36 \div 9 = 4$ $36 \div 4 = 9$
c. $6 \times 3 = 18$ $3 \times 6 = 18$ $18 \div 6 = 3$ $18 \div 3 = 6$
d. $5 \times 6 = 30$ $6 \times 5 = 30$ $30 \div 5 = 6$ $30 \div 6 = 5$
e. $9 \times 3 = 27$ $3 \times 9 = 27$ $27 \div 9 = 3$ $27 \div 3 = 9$
f. $7 \times 6 = 42$ $6 \times 7 = 42$ $42 \div 7 = 6$ $42 \div 6 = 7$
g. $8 \times 9 = 72$ $9 \times 8 = 72$ $72 \div 9 = 8$ $72 \div 8 = 9$

2.

a.	b.	c.	d.
45	18	7	6
24	42	3	4
64	20	5	7
27	32	5	4
24	49	3	7
24	21	6	2
30	40	9	4

3.
a.

IN	4	3	7	9	5	8
OUT	24	18	42	54	30	48

b.

IN	5	6	2	7	9	4
OUT	45	54	18	63	81	36

c.

IN	28	12	36	32	16	20
OUT	7	3	9	8	4	5

d.

IN	18	21	27	15	12	24
OUT	6	7	9	5	4	8

4.

a.

x	6	8	4
3	18	**24**	**12**
9	**54**	**72**	**36**
2	**12**	**16**	8

b.

x	4	9	3
8	**32**	**72**	**24**
7	**28**	**63**	**21**
5	**20**	**45**	**15**

c.

x	4	6	7
2	**8**	**12**	**14**
5	**20**	**30**	**35**
8	**32**	**48**	**56**

d.

x	4	**5**	8
2	8	10	**16**
3	12	**15**	24
6	**24**	30	**48**

e.

x	3	7	**9**
4	**12**	28	36
7	21	**49**	63
8	24	56	**72**

f.

x	**4**	6	**10**
3	12	18	30
5	20	**30**	50
10	40	60	100

Topic 6: **2D shapes** (page 14)

1.
✓**a.** triangle (regular)
b. triangle
c. rectangle or quadrilateral
✓**d.** hexagon (regular)
e. hexagon
f. triangle
✓**g.** square or rectangle or quadrilateral (regular)
h. quadrilateral
✓**i.** pentagon (regular)
j. quadrilateral
k. pentagon
l. octagon
m. decagon
n. nonagon
✓**o.** octagon (regular)
Tick a, d, g, i, o

2.
a. ✓ pentagons
b. ✓ quadrilaterals
c. ✓ heptagons
d. ✓ triangles
e. ✓ nonagons
f. ✓ octagons

3.

Test 1: (page 16)

1. 6047
2. 7000 + 200
3. 6047, 6704, 6740, 7064, 7604
4. 60,000
5. 14, 24, 34
6. 8
7. 120
8. 20
9. 13
10. 70
11. 16
12. 900
13. 8 cm, 6.5 km
14. 1.5 cm, 15 mm
15. 6.5 cm or 65 mm
16. 8 cm
17. 8 × 4 = 32 4 × 8 = 32 32 ÷ 4 = 8 32 ÷ 8 = 4
18. 42, 8
19. IN   4 7 6 9 8 2
     OUT 32 56 48 72 64 16

20.

x	3	8	7
4	12	32	28
6	18	48	42
9	27	72	63

21. pentagons

22. rectangle and quadrilateral
23. The pentagon is the odd one out; all the others are hexagons.
24. The two bottom corners are right angles.

Topic 7: **Time** (page 18)

1.
a. 7:20
b. 4:15
c. 6:55
d. 10:40
e. 8:17
f. 12:37
g. 5:03
h. 9:29

2.
a.
b.
c.
d.

3.

Church Street	8.50 a.m.	9.35 a.m.	11.00 a.m.	1.05 p.m.
Marsh Lane	9.15 a.m.	10.00 a.m.	11.25 a.m.	1.30 p.m.
Hospital	9.40 a.m.	10.25 a.m.	11.50 a.m.	1.55 p.m.
Swimming pool	10.05 a.m.	10.50 a.m.	12.15 p.m.	2.20 p.m.

4.
a. 8.05 p.m.
b. 1 hour and 25 minutes
c. 1.15 p.m.
d. 1.25 p.m.
e. 6 hours and 5 minutes

5.
a. 20 minutes slow
b. 40 minutes slow
c. 4 minutes slow
d. 16 minutes slow
e. 55 minutes slow
f. 36 minutes slow

Topic 8: **Fractions of shapes** (page 20)

1.
a. $\frac{1}{4}$
b. $\frac{1}{3}$
c. $\frac{1}{8}$
d. $\frac{1}{5}$
e. $\frac{1}{10}$
f. $\frac{1}{6}$
g. $\frac{2}{5}$
h. $\frac{3}{4}$
i. $\frac{3}{8}$
j. $\frac{4}{5}$
k. $\frac{9}{10}$
l. $\frac{4}{5}$

2.
a. $\frac{1}{3} = \frac{2}{6}$
b. $\frac{1}{2} = \frac{6}{12}$
c. $\frac{1}{5} = \frac{3}{15}$
d. $\frac{1}{4} = \frac{4}{16}$
e. $\frac{1}{2} = \frac{5}{10}$
f. $\frac{1}{4} = \frac{3}{12}$

3.
a. $\frac{1}{3}$
b. $\frac{3}{4}$
c. $\frac{1}{2}$
d. $\frac{1}{5}$
e. $\frac{3}{5}$
f. $\frac{1}{4}$

4.
a. Any 3 boxes should be shaded.
b. Any 2 boxes should be shaded.
c. Any 4 boxes should be shaded.
d. Any 4 boxes should be shaded.
e. Any 2 boxes should be shaded.
f. Any 3 boxes should be shaded.

5.
$\frac{1}{12}$ $\frac{1}{6}$ $\frac{1}{4}$ $\frac{1}{3}$ $\frac{1}{2}$ $\frac{2}{3}$ $\frac{3}{4}$ $\frac{5}{6}$

Topic 9: **Addition** (page 22)

1.
a. 110
b. 85
c. 60
d. 120
e. 115
f. 90
g. 130
h. 125
i. 100
j. 100
k. 105
l. 130

2.
a. 95
b. 115
c. 123
d. 98
e. 157
f. 76
g. 88
h. 79
i. 90
j. 89
k. 92
l. 82
m. 91
n. 91
o. 81
p. 126
q. 147
r. 131
s. 141
t. 142

3.

a.

53	47	**100**
28	31	**59**
81	**78**	**159**

b.

31	67	**98**
42	39	**81**
73	**106**	**179**

c.

62	57	**119**
38	29	**67**
100	**86**	**186**

d.

62	53	**115**
74	47	**121**
136	**100**	**236**

4.
74 → 37
68 → 43
67 → 44
47 → 64
78 → 33
57 → 54

5.
a. 28 + 67 = 95
b. 59 + 74 = 133
c. 81 + 64 = 145

Topic 10: Subtraction (page 24)

1.
a. 38 **b.** 37
c. 24 **d.** 24
e. 17 **f.** 28
g. 26 **h.** 29
i. 17 **j.** 35

2.
a. 21 **b.** 33 **c.** 22 **d.** 44
e. 34 **f.** 34 **g.** 27 **h.** 47
i. 38 **j.** 55 **k.** 36 **l.** 17
m. 25 **n.** 27 **o.** 38 **p.** 37
q. 27 **r.** 39 **s.** 25 **t.** 26

3.
a. 18 **b.** 16 **c.** 9 **d.** 16
e. 28 **f.** 17 **g.** 16 **h.** 25

4.
83 → 39
62 → 18
93 → 49
52 → 96
33 → 77
53 → 97

5.
a. 83 − 57 = 26   **b.** 94 − 68 = 26   **c.** 74 − 48 = 26

Topic 11: Sequences and patterns (page 26)

1.
a. 15, 17, 19   **b.** 27, 32, 37   **c.** 125, 127, 129   **d.** 270, 280, 290   **e.** 65, 60, 55
f. 500, 400, 300   **g.** 26, 29, 32   **h.** 18, 22, 26   **i.** 43, 40, 37   **j.** 160, 150, 140

2.
a. 24, 30, 36   **b.** 83, 58, 53   **c.** 410, 460, 710   **d.** 38, 46, 50   **e.** 99, 101, 109
f. 120, 125, 135   **g.** 82, 46, 28   **h.** 89, 73, 69   **i.** 47, 62, 65   **j.** 710, 510, 310

3.
a. −5, −4, 1, 2
b. −25, −20, 5, 10
c. −6, −5, 0, 1
d. −18, −15, 0, 3
e. −14, −12, −2, 0
f. −10, −7, 8, 11
g. −11, −9, 1, 3
h. −18, −14, 6, 10

4.
a. 35, 30
b. 31, 27
c. 43, 49
d. 468, 476
e. 910, 940
f. 144, 148

5.

1	2	3	4	5	6	7	8
9	10	11	12	13	14	15	16
17	18	19	20	21	22	23	24
25	26	27	28	29	30	31	32
33	34	35	36	37	38	39	40
41	42	43	44	45	46	47	48
49	50	51	52	53	54	55	56
57	58	59	60	61	62	63	64

Topic 12: Comparing and ordering numbers (page 28)

1.
a. 306, 368, 380, 800, 806, 860
b. 405, 450, 486, 589, 590, 594
c. 659, 689, 690, 906, 965, 966
d. 205, 215, 505, 512, 520, 522
e. 2599, 3005, 3125, 3152, 3502
f. 1670, 1706, 5799, 7509, 7611
g. 8079, 8095, 8307, 8345, 8543
h. 7244, 7323, 7324, 7332, 7342

2.
a. < **b.** < **c.** >
d. > **e.** > **f.** <
g. > **h.** > **i.** <

3.
a. 685 **b.** 4050
c. 530 **d.** 5690
e. 860 **f.** 1060
g. 390 **h.** 6475
i. 720 **j.** 8340

4.
a. < > **b.** > >
c. < < **d.** > <
e. < > **f.** > >

5.

Island	Area (sq km)
Great Britain	218 041
Iceland	103 000
Ireland	83 766
Sicily	25 400
Sardinia	23 800
Cyprus	9251
Corsica	8270
Crete	8260

Test 2 (page 30)

1. 6.12
2.
3. 50 minutes
4. 9.00
5. $\frac{3}{5}$
6. $\frac{1}{4} = \frac{2}{8}$
7. $\frac{1}{8}$
8. Any six boxes should be shaded
9. 165
10. 152
11.

53	47	**100**
28	31	**59**
81	**78**	**159**

12. 67 and 58
13. 38
14. 28
15. 45 and 93
16. 72 − 46 = 26
17. 28 and 33
18. 52 and 34
19. −14, −11, 4, 7
20. 37 and 41
21. 4679, 4767, 4769, 4799
22. 6105 < 6150
4355 > 4335
23. 4220
24. 6104 > 3259
< 3260

Topic 13: Rounding numbers (page 32)

1.
a. 460 **b.** 280
c. 150 **d.** 310
e. 640 **f.** 840
g. 1470 **h.** 9280

2.
a. 700 **b.** 500
c. 100 **d.** 600
e. 800 **f.** 900
g. 4900 **h.** 7800

3.
a. £1 **b.** £5
c. £2 **d.** £6
e. £5 **f.** £9
g. £13 **h.** £16

4.
These are estimates.
a. 20 50 70 90
b. 50 80 150 250
c. 60 90 130 180
d. 120 200 400 480

5.
These are estimates.
a. 200 400 700 900
b. 600 800 2300 2700
c. 500 900 1400 1800
d. 800 1900 3300 4700

6.
These are estimates.
a. 380 **b.** 5900
740 9600
170 2600
410 3300
600 80 000
1000 200 000

Topic 14: Weight and mass (page 34)

1.
a. 2500 g
b. 3250 g
c. 750 g
d. 10 500 g
e. 2750 g
f. 6500 g

2.
a. 2 kg 400 g
b. 1 kg 700 g
c. 3 kg 550 g
d. 5 kg 850 g
e. 1 kg 20 g
f. 4 kg 230 g

3.
a. 3 kg 500 g
b. 2 kg 500 g
c. 5 kg 500 g
d. 8 kg
e. 9 kg 600 g
f. 3 kg 900 g

4.
a. 2 kg
b. 300 g
c. E
d. 50 g
e. 800 g
f. D and F

5.
a. 4700 g
b. 5700 g
c. 2700 g
d. 2100 g
e. 4500 g
f. 3200 g

Topic 15: **3D shapes** (page 36)

1.
a. cone
b. tetrahedron
c. sphere
d. hemisphere
e. cube
f. square-based pyramid
g. cylinder

2.
a. Cube – all the others are cuboids
b. Cone – all the others are cylinders
c. Square-based pyramid – all the others are prisms
d. Prism – all the others are pyramids
e. Hemisphere – all the others are spheres

3.
a. 1 square face and 4 triangular faces
b. 2 triangular faces and 3 rectangular faces
c. 2 square faces and 4 rectangular faces
d. 4 triangular faces

4.
a. cube
b. tetrahedron
c. cuboid
d. hemisphere

Topic 16: **Multiplication** (page 38)

1.
a. 60 **b.** 120
c. 200 **d.** 210
e. 120 **f.** 250
g. 540 **h.** 270
i. 320 **j.** 140
k. 240 **l.** 140
m. 240 **n.** 360
o. 240

2.
a. 28 **b.** 34
c. 38 **d.** 46
e. 62 **f.** 56
g. 86 **h.** 94
i. 320 **j.** 500
k. 740 **l.** 980

3.
a. 180 **b.** 69
c. 185 **d.** 72
e. 210 **f.** 153
g. 315 **h.** 116
i. 256 **j.** 165
k. 276 **l.** 370
m. 172 **n.** 237
o. 352

4.
a. 258
b. 168
c. 98
d. 320
e. £152
f. 198

5.
a. 288
b. 371
c. 414
d. 468
e. 476
f. 632

6.
a. $23 \times 6 = 138$
b. $45 \times 7 = 315$
c. $68 \times 9 = 612$

Topic 17: **Division** (page 40)

1.
a. 8 **b.** 9 **c.** 9 **d.** 10 **e.** 7
f. 12 **g.** 7 **h.** 16 **i.** 15 **j.** 18
k. 24 **l.** 19 **m.** 17 **n.** 13 **o.** 23

2.
a. 17 **b.** 21 **c.** 19 **d.** 23
e. 16 **f.** 24 **g.** 28 **h.** 32
i. 41 **j.** 38 **k.** 47 **l.** 39

3.
a. 8 r 3 **b.** 8 r 2 **c.** 23 r 1
d. 14 r 2 **e.** 23 r 2 **f.** 41 r 1
g. 14 r 3 **h.** 14 r 4 **i.** 14 r 5

4.
a. 15
b. 49
c. 9
d. 14p
e. 11
f. 12

5.
$56 \div 6 \to 2$
$71 \div 8 \to 7$
$96 \div 5 \to 1$
$86 \div 8 \to 6$
$77 \div 9 \to 5$
$99 \div 10 \to 9$
$89 \div 9 \to 8$
$52 \div 7 \to 3$

Check that the remainder for the child's own division is 4.

6.
a. $75 \div 3 = 25$
b. $92 \div 2 = 46$
c. $12 \div 2 = 6$

Topic 18: **Coordinates** (page 42)

1.
A = (3, 2) F = (2, 3) D = (8, 4) H = (10, 4)
(5, 5) = B (0, 6) = G (4, 8) = E (1, 7) = C

2.
Check coordinates are plotted correctly.

3.

4.
Check child's coordinates are correct for the star drawn.

5.
a. A = (1, 3)
B = (3, 1)
C = (6, 4)
b. D = (4, 6)
c. Check corner D has been drawn in correctly at (4, 6).

Test 3 (page 44)

1. 540, 6450
2. 800, 3100
3. £4, £25
4. 80, 130, 150, 180 (these are estimates)
5. 8100 g
6. 6 kg 225 g
7. 6 kg 700 g
8. 3 kg 0 g
9. hemisphere
10. The odd one out is the pentagonal prism; all the others are cuboids.
11. 2 hexagonal faces and 6 rectangular faces

12. square-based pyramid
13. 280
14. 112
15. 249
16. 150
17. 16
18. 38
19. 19 r 2
20. 16p
21. (4, 0)
22. C
23. (6, 3)
24. Check the child's cross is correctly placed at (3, 5).

Topic 19: **Decimals** (page 46)

1.
a. 0.3 **b.** 0.9 **c.** 0.7 **d.** 0.5
e. 0.4 **f.** 0.8 **g.** 4.5 **h.** 2.1
i. 3.7 **j.** 5.3 **k.** 6.9 **l.** 4.2

2.
a. 0.3, 0.5, 0.6, 0.9
b. 0.1, 0.4, 0.7, 0.8
c. 1.2, 1.4, 1.5, 1.7
d. 2.1, 2.3, 2.6, 2.9
e. 3.2, 3.5, 3.7, 3.8
f. 0.2, 0.6, 1.4, 1.8

3.
a. $\frac{3}{10}$ **b.** $\frac{8}{10}$ **c.** $\frac{5}{100}$ **d.** $\frac{2}{100}$ **e.** $\frac{3}{10}$
f. $\frac{7}{100}$ **g.** $\frac{6}{10}$ **h.** $\frac{5}{100}$ **i.** $\frac{8}{10}$ **j.** $\frac{4}{10}$

4.
a. <
b. >
c. >
d. >
e. <
f. <
g. <
h. >

5.
a. 0.9, 2.9, 3, 3.1, 3.6, 3.8, 4
b. 0.4, 0.8, 4, 4.8, 8.1, 8.3, 8.32
c. 2, 2.1, 2.6, 2.71, 2.93, 7.17, 7.6
d. 3, 3.06, 10, 10.14, 10.35, 10.4, 11.1

Topic 20: **Capacity** (page 48)

1.
a. 1500 ml **b.** 2250 ml **c.** 250 ml **d.** 2100 ml
e. 6500 ml **f.** 4750 ml **g.** 8500 ml **h.** 12 300 ml

2.
a. 4 l 300 ml **b.** 1 l 900 ml **c.** 6 l 550 ml **d.** 2 l 350 ml
e. 2 l 20 ml **f.** 6 l 730 ml **g.** 4 l 525 ml **h.** 1 l 975 ml

3.
a. 700 ml **b.** 400 ml **c.** 100 ml **d.** 900 ml **e.** 800 ml
f. 1200 ml **g.** 1600 ml **h.** 1800 ml **i.** 1500 ml **j.** 1300 ml

4.
a. 1.5 l or 1½ l
b. 400 ml
c. C
d. 50 ml
e. 550 ml
f. F and D

5.
a. 2800 ml
b. 4800 ml
c. 3700 ml
d. 4100 ml
e. 3900 ml
f. 5300 ml

Topic 21: **Fractions of amounts** (page 50)

1.
a. 3 **b.** 2
5 4
4 1
6 3

2.
a. 5 **b.** 4 **c.** 5 **d.** 3
4 3 8 8
7 6 6 7
6 8 10 6
10 5 9 10

3.
a. $\frac{1}{2}$ **b.** $\frac{1}{10}$ **c.** $\frac{1}{4}$
$\frac{1}{5}$ $\frac{1}{2}$ $\frac{1}{2}$
$\frac{1}{10}$ $\frac{1}{4}$ $\frac{1}{10}$
$\frac{1}{4}$ $\frac{3}{4}$ $\frac{3}{4}$
$\frac{3}{4}$ $\frac{1}{5}$ $\frac{1}{5}$

4.
a. $\frac{1}{10}$ **b.** $\frac{1}{4}$ **c.** $\frac{1}{2}$
$\frac{4}{10}$ or $\frac{2}{5}$ $\frac{3}{4}$ $\frac{1}{4}$
$\frac{2}{10}$ or $\frac{1}{5}$ $\frac{6}{10}$ or $\frac{3}{5}$ $\frac{1}{10}$
$\frac{1}{2}$ $\frac{8}{10}$ or $\frac{4}{5}$ $\frac{3}{4}$
$\frac{3}{10}$ $\frac{7}{10}$ $\frac{2}{10}$ or $\frac{1}{5}$

5.
Check that the triangles coloured are as
follows
6 triangles red
4 triangles blue
2 triangles yellow
8 triangles green
3 triangles orange
1 triangle will be left white

Topic 22: **Graphs** (page 52)

1.
a. 40
b. Friday
c. Tuesday and Sunday
d. 16–19
e. Wednesday and Thursday
f. 26
g. 48
h. The museum was probably closed.

2.
a. 78
b. December
c. November
d. 105
e. September

3.
Check that the graph
has been completed
correctly.
a. Chris
b. David
c. Eric
d. Chris, Fred, Eric,
David, Alan, Ben

Topic 23: **Money** (page 54)

1.
a. 40p **b.** 73p **c.** 33p **d.** 20p
e. 81p **f.** 90p **g.** 57p **h.** 70p
i. 74p **j.** 72p

2.
a. 125p **b.** 349p **c.** 208p **d.** 1499p
e. 1281p **f.** 2306p **g.** £1.49 **h.** £2.27
i. £5.03 **j.** £12.31 **k.** £14.66 **l.** £0.69

3.
a. 52p **b.** 70p **c.** £1.25
15p £2.11 78p
63p £1.79 £3.01
36p 94p £5.17
9p £2.03 £2.44
71p £3.16 £1.53

4.
a. £1.80
b. 8
c. £3.72
d. £2.80
e. £3.27
f. £5.02

5.
a. £1.89
b. £2.50
c. £3.80
d. £2.14

6.
a. Check which 5 coins add to each
of the four amounts.
b. Check which 6 coins add to each
of the four amounts.
c. Lowest possible amount with 6
different coins is
88p → 1p + 2p + 5p + 10p +
20p + 50p coins

Topic 24: **Angles** (page 56)

1.
a. 45° **b.** 90°
c. 180° **d.** 90°
e. 180° **f.** 45°
g. 360° **h.** 60°
i. 60° **j.** 360°

2.
a. S **b.** W
c. NE **d.** E
e. SW **f.** N
g. E **h.** S
i. NE **j.** E
k. NW **l.** S

3.
There are 16 right angles altogether.

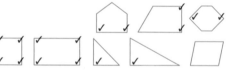

4.
F, D, B, A, C, E

5.
a. 180° **b.** WASH
60° OFF
180° DRY
240° OFF

Test 4 (page 58)

1. 0.3, 0.5
2. 0.4, 0.7
3. $\frac{5}{10}$
4. 4.6 < 4.8 > 4.3
5. 3100 ml
6. 4 l 805 ml
7. 1 l 400 ml
8. 700 ml
9. 4
10. 6
11. $\frac{1}{4}$
12. $\frac{3}{4}$
13. 23
14. rabbit
15. 6
16. 14
17. 77p
18. 376p, £12.45
19. £3.11
20. 32p
21. 180°
22. All four corners
should be ticked
on the rectangle.
23. NW
24.